Contents

C000183122

Introduction

This book forms part of the *No Nonsense Number* series that supports learning in learning in Years 6 and 7.

Where a calculator appears at the top right of a page, it is indicating that the children are to use a calculator to complete that particular page.

A pupil template has been included as one of the activity sheets, as a way of reinforcing selected specific learning objectives. For this template, children develop their own problems for other pupils to solve. Templates have also been included in the activity cards (games) section for either the class teacher or the pupil to fill in the appropriate numbers and extend the game.

Answers to the problems are provided at the end of this book. Unless otherwise specified, the fractions have not been simplified. However, you may choose to encourage your pupils to do this.

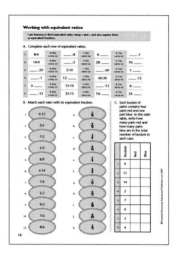

Curriculum Links

Strand: Number	
Substrand	**Learning objectives** *Pupils should:*
Year 7	
2.1 Place value, ordering and rounding	• understand and use decimal notation and place value; multiply and divide integers by 10, 100, 1000, and explain the effect • compare and order decimals • round decimals to the nearest whole number or one decimal place
2.2 Integers, powers and roots	• use simple tests of divisibility • recognise and use lowest common multiples
2.3 Fractions, decimals, percentages, ratio and proportion	• simplify fractions by cancelling all common factors and identify equivalent fractions. • add and subtract simple fractions and those with common denominators; calculate simple fractions of quantities and measurements (whole-number answers); multiply a fraction by an integer • understand percentage as the 'number of parts per 100'; calculate simple percentages • recognise the equivalence of percentages, fractions and decimals • use ratio notation, simplify ratios and divide a quantity into two parts in a given ratio
2.4 Number operations	• understand and use the rules of arithmetic and inverse operations in the context of positive integers and decimals
2.5 Mental calculation methods	• strengthen and extend mental methods of calculation to include decimals, fractions and percentages, accompanied where appropriate by suitable jottings; solve simple problems mentally • make and justify estimates and approximations of calculations
Year 8	
2.2 Integers, powers and roots	• use index notation for small positive integer powers

Source: Adapted from *The Framework for secondary mathematics, 2008*

No Nonsense Number

Activities to support learning in Years 6 and 7

Part C

Suzi de Gouveia,
Jackie Andrews
and Jude Callaghan

essential
resources

essential
resources

Title: No Nonsense Number
Activities to support Learning in Years 6 and 7 – Part C

Authors: Suzi de Gouveia, Jackie Andrews and Jude Callaghan

Editor: Tanya Tremewan

Book code: 293C

ISBN: 978-1-877523-06-9

Published: 2009

Publisher: Essential Resources Educational Publishers Limited

United Kingdom:	**Australia:**	**New Zealand:**
Unit 8–10 Parkside	PO Box 90	PO Box 5036
Shortgate Lane	Oak Flats	Invercargill
Laughton, BN8 6DG	NSW 2529	
ph: 0845 3636 147	ph: 1800 005 068	ph: 0800 087 376
fax: 0845 3636 148	fax: 1800 981 213	fax: 0800 937 825

Website: www.essentialresourcesuk.com

Copyright: Text: © Suzi de Gouveia, Jackie Andrews and Jude Callaghan, 2009
Edition and Illustrations: © Essential Resources Educational Publishers Limited, 2009

About the authors: Suzi is the enthusiastic headteacher of St Teresa's Primary School in Christchurch, New Zealand. She has international teaching experience and has had the pleasure of teaching in a multi-cultural environment. Over 20 years of teaching have enabled Suzi to develop a wealth of ideas and resources to best help children.

Jackie is an experienced teacher who has taught primary children in both New Zealand and the United Kingdom. As a mother of three young children she is taking time out of the classroom and is enjoying having the time to diversify.

Jude is an experienced, enthusiastic teacher with a passion for teaching and learning. Her teaching programmes are innovative and exciting. She has joined the No Nonsense Number writing team to share her deep understanding and wealth of ideas.

Ordering and rounding decimals, percentages and fractions

I am learning to order and round decimals.

For each group of pupils, order these decimals from **smallest** to **biggest**, put an arrow on the number line to show where the largest number goes and round each number to two decimal places.

A.

| 6.324981 | 6.32981 | 6.32986 | 6.324891 |

1. _____   _____   _____   _____

2.

6.324   6.33

3. Rounding:

_____   _____   _____   _____

B.

| 2.787922 | 2.788010 | 2.788001 | 2.787977 |

1. _____   _____   _____   _____

2.

2.7878   2.7881

3. Rounding:

_____   _____   _____   _____

C.

| 0.27564 | 0.27584 | 0.27559 | 0.27523 |

1. _____   _____   _____   _____

2.

0.2752   0.2758

3. Rounding:

_____   _____   _____   _____

For each group of pupils order these decimals from **smallest** to **biggest**, put an arrow on the number line to show where the largest number goes and round each number to two decimal places.

A.

| 2.324981 | 2.32981 | 2.32986 | 2.324891 |

1. _____   _____   _____   _____

2.

2.325   2.33

3. Rounding:

_____   _____   _____   _____

B.

| 77.2336 | 77.2292 | 77.2351 | 77.2308 |

1. _____   _____   _____   _____

2.

77.229   77.234

3. Rounding:

_____   _____   _____   _____

C.

| 0.022154 | 0.022185 | 0.022177 | 0.022169 |

1. _____   _____   _____   _____

2.
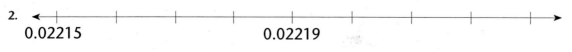

0.02215   0.02219

3. Rounding:

_____   _____   _____   _____

Order each group of numbers from **smallest** to **biggest** to find out which mouse ate the most problems.

1.

$\frac{5}{8}$ 75%   0.62

_____ _____ _____

2.

$\frac{2}{3}$ 60%   0.54

_____ _____ _____

3.

$\frac{4}{32}$ 10%   0.25

_____ _____ _____

4.

$\frac{4}{5}$ 0.85 $\frac{84}{100}$

_____ _____ _____

5.

0.7   65% $\frac{3}{5}$

_____ _____ _____

6.

26% $\frac{2}{8}$ 0.2

_____ _____ _____

7.

$\frac{16}{64}$ 0.2   15%

_____ _____ _____

8.

65% $\frac{24}{40}$ 0.75

_____ _____ _____

9.

0.7   65% $\frac{28}{42}$

_____ _____ _____

10.

$\frac{5}{40}$ 0.1   15%

_____ _____ _____

11.

59% $\frac{4}{6}$ 0.6

_____ _____ _____

12.

0.3 $\frac{3}{8}$ 33%

_____ _____ _____

7

I am learning to order fractions, decimals and percentages.

Each pupil has run a proportion of the cross-country race. Order the numbers in each row from **smallest** to **biggest**. Write them in the correct order on the lines below.

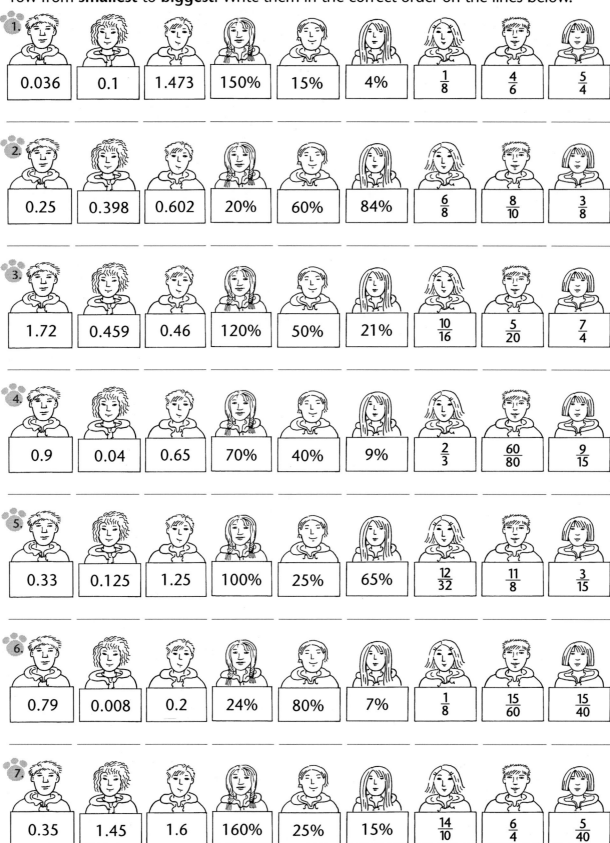

1. | 0.036 | 0.1 | 1.473 | 150% | 15% | 4% | $\frac{1}{8}$ | $\frac{4}{6}$ | $\frac{5}{4}$ |

_____

2. | 0.25 | 0.398 | 0.602 | 20% | 60% | 84% | $\frac{6}{8}$ | $\frac{8}{10}$ | $\frac{3}{8}$ |

_____

3. | 1.72 | 0.459 | 0.46 | 120% | 50% | 21% | $\frac{10}{16}$ | $\frac{5}{20}$ | $\frac{7}{4}$ |

_____

4. | 0.9 | 0.04 | 0.65 | 70% | 40% | 9% | $\frac{2}{3}$ | $\frac{60}{80}$ | $\frac{9}{15}$ |

_____

5. | 0.33 | 0.125 | 1.25 | 100% | 25% | 65% | $\frac{12}{32}$ | $\frac{11}{8}$ | $\frac{3}{15}$ |

_____

6. | 0.79 | 0.008 | 0.2 | 24% | 80% | 7% | $\frac{1}{8}$ | $\frac{15}{60}$ | $\frac{15}{40}$ |

_____

7. | 0.35 | 1.45 | 1.6 | 160% | 25% | 15% | $\frac{14}{10}$ | $\frac{6}{4}$ | $\frac{5}{40}$ |

_____

A. Place the symbol < , > or = in each box to make the relationship true.

1.	$\frac{3}{4}$	☐	0.65	☐	70%		15.	$\frac{24}{40}$	☐	0.85	☐	60%
2.	$\frac{10}{16}$	☐	0.75	☐	60%		16.	$\frac{3}{8}$	☐	0.375	☐	35%
3.	$\frac{4}{5}$	☐	0.6	☐	50%		17.	$\frac{10}{15}$	☐	0.5	☐	5%
4.	$\frac{10}{15}$	☐	0.7	☐	75%		18.	$\frac{20}{25}$	☐	0.65	☐	70%
5.	$\frac{6}{4}$	☐	1.25	☐	120%		19.	$\frac{20}{30}$	☐	0.06	☐	60%
6.	$\frac{4}{12}$	☐	0.33	☐	40%		20.	$\frac{50}{80}$	☐	0.725	☐	70%
7.	$\frac{10}{80}$	☐	0.125	☐	15%		21.	$\frac{16}{20}$	☐	0.75	☐	75%
8.	$\frac{15}{40}$	☐	0.25	☐	20%		22.	$\frac{4}{32}$	☐	0.12	☐	10%
9.	$\frac{12}{20}$	☐	0.04	☐	40%		23.	$\frac{12}{15}$	☐	1.4	☐	14%
10.	$\frac{9}{12}$	☐	0.85	☐	90%		24.	$\frac{7}{21}$	☐	0.45	☐	50%
11.	$\frac{15}{20}$	☐	0.75	☐	70%		25.	$\frac{25}{40}$	☐	0.625	☐	62.5%
12.	$\frac{9}{36}$	☐	0.2	☐	25%		26.	$\frac{4}{6}$	☐	0.6	☐	6%
13.	$\frac{5}{4}$	☐	1.4	☐	140%		27.	$\frac{15}{60}$	☐	0.25	☐	2.5%
14.	$\frac{19}{8}$	☐	2.5	☐	150%		28.	$\frac{3}{9}$	☐	0.333	☐	30%

B. Order the numbers in each row from **smallest** to **biggest**. Write them in the correct order on the lines below.

| 0.62 | 0.2 | 0.1 | 33% | 15% | 50% | $\frac{4}{20}$ | $\frac{9}{24}$ | $\frac{12}{18}$ |

_____

| 1.4 | 0.8 | 0.7 | 120% | 75% | 90% | $\frac{9}{8}$ | $\frac{8}{12}$ | $\frac{4}{3}$ |

_____

Skip-counting in hundredths

I am learning to skip-count forwards and backwards in hundredths.

Fill in the missing numbers. Count on and back in hundredths. The first row is started for you.

	− 0.01	− 0.01	− 0.01		+ 0.01	+ 0.01	+ 0.01
1.				0.129	0.139		
2.				2.069			
3.				8.036			
4.				0.069			
5.				0.128			
6.				0.971			
7.				0.999			
8.				0.479			
9.				4.021			
10.				8.003			
11.				7.048			
12.				0.149			
13.				6.028			
14.				0.159			
15.				4.035			
16.				2.396			
17.				1.009			
18.				8.225			
19.				0.548			
20.				6.039			
21.				4.605			
22.				1.024			
23.				3.981			
24.				1.001			

Dividing and multiplying by powers of 10

I am learning to recall what happens when a whole number is divided by powers of 10.

A. Fill in the answer to each equation.

1. $40 \div 10^0 =$ _____

2. $110 \div 10^1 =$ _____

3. $1\ 100\ 000 \div 10^3 =$ _____

4. $95\ 000 \div 10^1 =$ _____

5. $73\ 000 \div 10^1 =$ _____

6. $520 \div 10^0 =$ _____

7. $30\ 000 \div 10^2 =$ _____

8. $5\ 100 \div 10^3 =$ _____

9. $87\ 000 \div 10^2 =$ _____

10. $4\ 900 \div 10^2 =$ _____

11. $4\ 700 \div 10^2 =$ _____

12. $2\ 000 \div 10^2 =$ _____

13. $290 \div 10^0 =$ _____

14. $540\ 000 \div 10^2 =$ _____

15. $910\ 000 \div 10^3 =$ _____

16. $7\ 700\ 000 \div 10^3 =$ _____

B. Fill in the blank in each equation. Your answer should be a whole number to a power of 10.

1. $90 \div$ _____ $= 9$

2. $670 \div$ _____ $= 67$

3. $1\ 300\ 000 \div$ _____ $= 13\ 000$

4. $28\ 000 \div$ _____ $= 280$

5. $43\ 000 \div$ _____ $= 430$

6. $910 \div$ _____ $= 91$

7. $80\ 000 \div$ _____ $= 80$

8. $4\ 300 \div$ _____ $= 430$

9. $86\ 000 \div$ _____ $= 8\ 600$

10. $7\ 300 \div$ _____ $= 730$

11. $4\ 900 \div$ _____ $= 49$

12. $6\ 000 \div$ _____ $= 60$

13. $730 \div$ _____ $= 73$

14. $130\ 000 \div$ _____ $= 1\ 300$

15. $790\ 000 \div$ _____ $= 7\ 900$

16. $3\ 700\ 000 \div$ _____ $= 370\ 000$

C. Solve these problems.

1. Mike got into his time machine and travelled 730 000 km at a speed of 10^3 km per hour. How many hours was Mike in the time machine?

   _____

2. Theo got into his time machine and travelled 650 000 000 km at a speed of 10^5 km per hour. How many hours was Theo in the time machine?

   _____

I am learning to recall what happens when a whole number is multiplied by powers of 10.

A. Fill in the answer to each equation.

1. $34 \times 10^0 =$ _____
2. $14 \times 10^3 =$ _____
3. $6\,900 \times 10^0 =$ _____
4. $910 \times 10^2 =$ _____
5. $8\,200 \times 10^2 =$ _____
6. $5\,300 \times 10^0 =$ _____
7. $1 \times 10^0 =$ _____
8. $5\,100 \times 10^3 =$ _____
9. $140 \times 10^2 =$ _____
10. $50 \times 10^2 =$ _____
11. $1\,000 \times 10^2 =$ _____
12. $6\,400 \times 10^3 =$ _____
13. $730 \times 10^2 =$ _____
14. $5\,600 \times 10^2 =$ _____
15. $1\,500 \times 10^1 =$ _____
16. $80 \times 10^0 =$ _____

B. Fill in the blank in each equation. Your answer should be a whole number to a power of 10.

1. $560 \times$ _____ $= 560$
2. $840 \times$ _____ $= 840\,000$
3. $96\,000 \times$ _____ $= 960\,000$
4. $752 \times$ _____ $= 75\,200$
5. $640 \times$ _____ $= 64\,000$
6. $2\,400 \times$ _____ $= 24\,000$
7. $98\,700 \times$ _____ $= 987\,000$
8. $7\,300 \times$ _____ $= 730\,000$
9. $140 \times$ _____ $= 14\,000$
10. $900 \times$ _____ $= 9\,000$
11. $93\,600 \times$ _____ $= 9\,360\,000$
12. $62\,300 \times$ _____ $= 623\,000$
13. $910 \times$ _____ $= 910$
14. $250 \times$ _____ $= 250\,000$
15. $87\,400 \times$ _____ $= 874\,000$
16. $95 \times$ _____ $= 9\,500\,000$

C. Solve these problems.

1. Jude went on a trip to space. She travelled for three hours at a speed of 10^3 km per hour. How far did she travel?

_____

2. Suzi went on a trip to space. She travelled for five hours at a speed of 10^4 km per hour. How far did she travel?

_____

© Essential Resources Educational Publishers Ltd, 2009

Solving multiplication and division problems with exponents

A. Fill in the missing numbers. The first one has been started for you.

1. $2^3 \times 2^{\boxed{5}} = 2^8$

   $= ($ ___ $2 \times 2 \times 2$ ___ $) \times ($ _____ $)$

   $= $ ___ 8 ___ $\times$ _____

   $= $ _____

2. $5^2 \times 5^\square = 5^6$

   $= ($ _____ $) \times ($ _____ $)$

   $= $ _____ $\times$ _____

   $= $ _____

3. $2^2 \times 2^\square = 2^6$

   $= ($ _____ $) \times ($ _____ $)$

   $= $ _____ $\times$ _____

   $= $ _____

4. $10^4 \times 10^\square = 10^6$

   $= ($ _____ $) \times ($ _____ $)$

   $= $ _____ $\times$ _____

   $= $ _____

5. $2^\square \times 2^4 = 2^9$

   $= ($ _____ $) \times ($ _____ $)$

   $= $ _____ $\times$ _____

   $= $ _____

6. $10^5 \times 10^\square = 10^9$

   $= ($ _____ $) \times ($ _____ $)$

   $= $ _____ $\times$ _____

   $= $ _____

B. Now complete these problems in your book.

1. $3^2 \times 3^\square = 3^7$

2. $10^3 \times 10^\square = 10^5$

3. $3^3 \times 3^\square = 3^5$

4. $5^3 \times 5^\square = 5^5$

5. $3^\square \times 3^3 = 3^8$

6. $5^3 \times 5^\square = 5^3$

13

A. Fill in the missing numbers. The first one has been started for you.

B. Now complete these problems in your book.

1. $4^6 \div 4^3 = 4^{\boxed{3}}$

= (_____) × (_____)

= _____ × _____

= _____

1. $4^9 \div 4^6 = 4^{\square}$

2. $2^5 \div 2^2 = 2^{\square}$

= (_____) × (_____)

= _____ × _____

= _____

2. $4^8 \div 4^4 = 4^{\square}$

3. $3^6 \div 3^4 = 3^{\square}$

= (_____) × (_____)

= _____ × _____

= _____

3. $5^7 \div 5^5 = 5^{\square}$

4. $2^5 \div 2^4 = 2^{\square}$

= (_____) × (_____)

= _____ × _____

= _____

4. $2^9 \div 2^3 = 2^{\square}$

5. $3^7 \div 3^5 = 3^{\square}$

= (_____) × (_____)

= _____ × _____

= _____

5. $3^8 \div 3^7 = 3^{\square}$

6. $5^3 \div 5^2 = 5^{\square}$

= (_____) × (_____)

= _____ × _____

= _____

6. $4^{10} \div 4^2 = 4^{\square}$

14

Working out percentages

I am learning to work out percentages.

A. Write the simple fractions in the middle box to help you find the percentage. The first one is started for you.

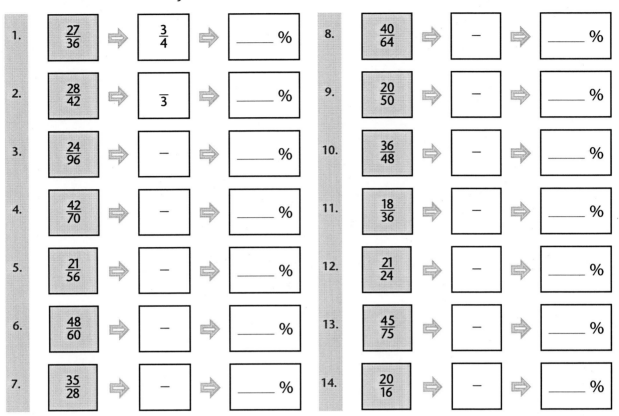

1. $\frac{27}{36}$ ⇒ $\frac{3}{4}$ ⇒ _____ %
2. $\frac{28}{42}$ ⇒ $\frac{}{3}$ ⇒ _____ %
3. $\frac{24}{96}$ ⇒ — ⇒ _____ %
4. $\frac{42}{70}$ ⇒ — ⇒ _____ %
5. $\frac{21}{56}$ ⇒ — ⇒ _____ %
6. $\frac{48}{60}$ ⇒ — ⇒ _____ %
7. $\frac{35}{28}$ ⇒ — ⇒ _____ %

8. $\frac{40}{64}$ ⇒ — ⇒ _____ %
9. $\frac{20}{50}$ ⇒ — ⇒ _____ %
10. $\frac{36}{48}$ ⇒ — ⇒ _____ %
11. $\frac{18}{36}$ ⇒ — ⇒ _____ %
12. $\frac{21}{24}$ ⇒ — ⇒ _____ %
13. $\frac{45}{75}$ ⇒ — ⇒ _____ %
14. $\frac{20}{16}$ ⇒ — ⇒ _____ %

B. Maria, June, Sally and Gurjit were shoots in a netball tournament. Work out the shooting percentage for each girl in each game.

Game 1

		Number of shots attempted	Number of shots in	Percentage
1.	Maria	48	18	
2.	June	72	48	
3.	Sally	45	36	
4.	Gurjit	24	18	

Game 2

		Number of shots attempted	Number of shots in	Percentage
5.	Maria	35	28	
6.	June	40	25	
7.	Sally	60	36	
8.	Gurjit	42	14	

Learning divisibility rules

I am learning the divisibility rules for 2, 3, 4, 5, 6, 9, 10 and 15.

These pupils have given an answer that they think is right. Circle whether you agree or disagree and write why. Correct the answer if you need to.

1.

I think 367 596 is divisible by 2 and 4 only.

Agree / Disagree
Why?
Corrections

2.

I think 695 275 is divisible by 5 and 15 only.

Agree / Disagree
Why?
Corrections

3.

I think 27 834 is divisible by 2, 3 and 6.

Agree / Disagree
Why?
Corrections

4.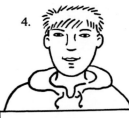

I think 723 192 is divisible by 2, 3, 4 and 9 only.

Agree / Disagree
Why?
Corrections

5.

I think 784 290 is divisible by 2, 5, 10 and 3.

Agree / Disagree
Why?
Corrections

6.

I think 17 208 is divisible by 2, 3, 9 and 6 only.

Agree / Disagree
Why?
Corrections

7.

I think 184 050 is divisible by 5, 2 and 10 only.

Agree / Disagree
Why?
Corrections

8.

I think 682 432 is divisible by 2, 4 and 3 only.

Agree / Disagree
Why?
Corrections

I am learning the divisibility rules for 2, 3, 4, 5, 6, 9, 10 and 15.

On each pupil card, write a statement that begins with 'I think...' and includes a big number along with possible numbers that will divide into it. Make some statements true and some false. Give your sheet to a maths buddy to complete.

These pupils have given an answer that they think is right. Circle whether you agree or disagree and write why. Correct the answer if you need to.

Working with equivalent ratios

I am learning to find equivalent ratios using × and ÷ and also express them as equivalent fractions.

A. Complete each row of equivalent ratios.

1.	8:4	is the same as	____ :8	is the same as	4: ____	is the same as	____ :1
2.	14:4	is the same as	____ :2	is the same as	28: ____	is the same as	70: ____
3.	____ :20	is the same as	2:10	is the same as	____ :60	is the same as	1: ____
4.	____ :1	is the same as	12: ____	is the same as	60:30	is the same as	____ :12
5.	3: ____	is the same as	15:10	is the same as	____ :12	is the same as	6: ____
6.	____ :12	is the same as	25:15	is the same as	10: ____	is the same as	35: ____

B. Match each ratio with its equivalent fraction.

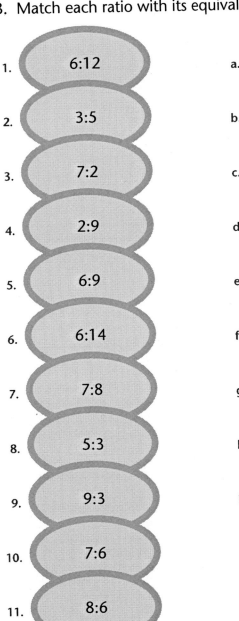

1. 6:12
2. 3:5
3. 7:2
4. 2:9
5. 6:9
6. 6:14
7. 7:8
8. 5:3
9. 9:3
10. 7:6
11. 8:6

a. $\frac{7}{13}$
b. $\frac{9}{12}$
c. $\frac{3}{8}$
d. $\frac{8}{14}$
e. $\frac{7}{9}$
f. $\frac{5}{8}$
g. $\frac{7}{15}$
h. $\frac{6}{15}$
i. $\frac{6}{18}$
j. $\frac{6}{20}$
k. $\frac{2}{11}$

C. Each bucket of paint contains four parts red and one part blue. In this ratio table, write how many parts red and how many parts blue are in the total number of buckets in each case.

	Buckets	Red	Blue
1.	9		
2.	11		
3.	14		
4.	2		
5.	7		
6.	6		
7.	5		
8.	4		

Finding ratios of whole numbers

I am learning to find ratios of whole numbers.

A. Brendan is an army cook. He has decided to produce a recipe book with his best recipes in it for the public to use. Help him complete the conversion table.

Spaghetti bolognaise for 100 people
10 kg mince   2 kg mushrooms
1 kg tomatoes   250 g mixed herbs

	Number of people to feed	Mince (grams)	Mushrooms (grams)	Tomatoes (grams)	Mixed herbs (grams)
1.	100	10 000			
2.		5 000			
3.				250	
4.			100		
5.					2.5

B. Tilly and Helen went fruit picking during their school holidays. Tilly worked longer hours than Helen. They made £500 in the first week and decided to split their earnings 3:2.

1. How much did each girl get in the first week?   _____

   For their second week they split their earnings 5:3.

2. If Tilly made £150, how much did Helen make?   _____

C. The new jellybean supervisor has given you the ratios that are shaded on the table below to use when you fill the jellybean packets. With these ratios in mind, complete the table.

	Red	Orange	Blue	Green	Black
	3	1	2	4	1
1.	6				
2.			8		
3.				20	
4.		3			
5.					9
6.	21				

Adding and subtracting fractions

I am learning to add fractions with different denominators.

A. Find the lowest common denominator (LCD) for each pair of fractions.

1. $\frac{6}{16}$ $\frac{3}{4}$ LCD ____

2. $\frac{3}{5}$ $\frac{1}{2}$ LCD ____

3. $\frac{2}{9}$ $\frac{1}{4}$ LCD ____

4. $\frac{3}{4}$ $\frac{4}{5}$ LCD ____

5. $\frac{2}{3}$ $\frac{1}{5}$ LCD ____

6. $\frac{6}{9}$ $\frac{1}{3}$ LCD ____

B. Link each problem on the left with the box containing the lowest common denominator. Then write the equivalent problem and finally the answer. One is started for you.

		LCD	Equivalent problem	Answer
1.	$\frac{5}{9} + \frac{1}{2}$	15	$\frac{6}{15} + \frac{}{15}$	____
2.	$\frac{3}{4} + \frac{2}{6}$	9		____
3.	$\frac{2}{3} + \frac{3}{9}$	18		____
4.	$\frac{3}{8} + \frac{1}{3}$	12		____
5.	$\frac{4}{5} + \frac{1}{2}$	24		____
6.	$\frac{2}{5} + \frac{1}{3}$	10		____

C. Solve these problems.

1. Wilber and his friends went to Peter's Pizza Parlour and ordered several pizzas. Wilber ate $\frac{7}{8}$, Jack ate $\frac{2}{5}$, Nathan ate $\frac{3}{4}$ and Josh ate $\frac{1}{2}$ of a pizza. How much pizza did they eat altogether?

____

2. Heulwen and Geraldine had a competition to see who could fit the most marshmallows in their mouth. Heulwen managed $\frac{3}{5}$ of a bag. Geraldine managed $\frac{5}{8}$ of a bag. What fraction of the two bags of marshmallows was left over?

____

© Essential Resources Educational Publishers Ltd, 2009

I am learning to add fractions with different denominators using three fractions.

A. Find the lowest common denominator (LCD) for each group of fractions.

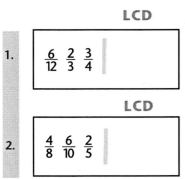

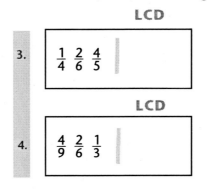

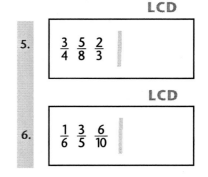

LCD

1. $\frac{6}{12}$ $\frac{2}{3}$ $\frac{3}{4}$

LCD

3. $\frac{1}{4}$ $\frac{2}{6}$ $\frac{4}{5}$

LCD

5. $\frac{3}{4}$ $\frac{5}{8}$ $\frac{2}{3}$

LCD

2. $\frac{4}{8}$ $\frac{6}{10}$ $\frac{2}{5}$

LCD

4. $\frac{4}{9}$ $\frac{2}{6}$ $\frac{1}{3}$

LCD

6. $\frac{1}{6}$ $\frac{3}{5}$ $\frac{6}{10}$

B. Link each problem on the left with the box containing the lowest common denominator. Then write the equivalent problem and finally the answer.

	LCD	Equivalent problem	Answer
1. $\frac{1}{4} + \frac{6}{10} + \frac{2}{8}$	30	$\frac{}{30} + \frac{}{30} + \frac{}{30}$	_____
2. $\frac{2}{5} + \frac{2}{3} + \frac{1}{6}$	24		_____
3. $\frac{1}{4} + \frac{1}{2} + \frac{4}{6}$	12		_____
4. $\frac{3}{8} + \frac{1}{4} + \frac{2}{6}$	36		_____
5. $\frac{3}{5} + \frac{1}{2} + \frac{1}{4}$	40		_____
6. $\frac{4}{9} + \frac{1}{2} + \frac{3}{4}$	20		_____

C. Solve these problems.

1. Ben, Tom and Becs went apple picking. Ben picked $\frac{7}{8}$ of his row of trees. Tom picked $\frac{1}{2}$ of his row and Becs picked $\frac{5}{6}$ of her row of trees.

What fraction of the three rows of trees were picked altogether?

_____

2. Heulwen, Geraldine and Nicola got a job gathering sea slugs. Heulwen gathered $\frac{3}{4}$ of her bucket, Geraldine gathered $\frac{1}{2}$ of her bucket and Nicola gathered $\frac{5}{6}$ of her bucket.

How many buckets did they gather altogether?

_____

I am learning to add and subtract fractions.

A. Write out each equation, filling in the missing numbers as you go.

1. $\dfrac{4}{5} + \dfrac{\square}{6} = \dfrac{\square}{30} + \dfrac{25}{30} = \dfrac{\square}{30} = 1\dfrac{19}{30}$

_____

2. $\dfrac{2}{3} - \dfrac{\square}{4} = \dfrac{\square}{12} - \dfrac{3}{12} = \dfrac{\square}{12}$

_____

3. $\dfrac{2}{5} + \dfrac{\square}{3} = \dfrac{\square}{15} + \dfrac{\square}{15} = \dfrac{11}{15}$

_____

4. $\dfrac{7}{9} - \dfrac{\square}{2} = \dfrac{\square}{18} - \dfrac{\square}{18} = \dfrac{5}{18}$

_____

5. $\dfrac{3}{8} + \dfrac{\square}{3} = \dfrac{\square}{24} + \dfrac{\square}{24} = \dfrac{\square}{\square} = 1\dfrac{1}{24}$

_____

6. $\dfrac{\square}{8} - \dfrac{\square}{5} = \dfrac{30}{\square} - \dfrac{\square}{40} = \dfrac{14}{40}$

_____

7. $\dfrac{\square}{4} - \dfrac{\square}{6} = \dfrac{9}{\square} - \dfrac{\square}{\square} = \dfrac{5}{12}$

_____

8. $\dfrac{\square}{3} + \dfrac{3}{\square} = \dfrac{10}{\square} + \dfrac{\square}{15} = \dfrac{\square}{15} = \square\dfrac{\square}{15}$

_____

B. Use the work space provided to work out the missing number in each equation.

1. $\dfrac{3}{7} + \dfrac{\square}{3} = \dfrac{16}{21}$

2. $\dfrac{\square}{9} - \dfrac{2}{3} = \dfrac{1}{9}$

3. $\dfrac{\square}{3} - \dfrac{1}{5} = \dfrac{7}{15}$

4. $\dfrac{2}{5} + \dfrac{\square}{8} = \dfrac{31}{40}$

5. $\dfrac{7}{9} - \dfrac{\square}{4} = \dfrac{1}{36}$

6. $\dfrac{\square}{9} - \dfrac{1}{2} = \dfrac{3}{18}$

7. $\dfrac{2}{5} + \dfrac{\square}{6} = \dfrac{22}{30}$

8. $\dfrac{\square}{5} + \dfrac{1}{2} = \dfrac{11}{10}$

I am learning to subtract fractions with different denominators.

A. Find the lowest common denominator (LCD) and the equivalent fractions (EF) for each group of fractions.

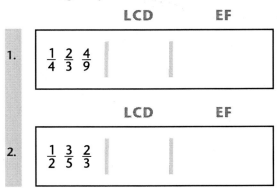

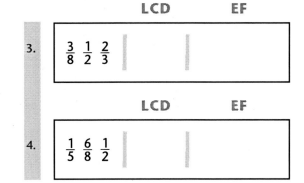

B. For each problem, write the equivalent problem and then the answer. Some have been started for you.

	Problem		Equivalent problem		Answer
1.	$\frac{2}{3} - \frac{1}{2}$	→	$\frac{}{6} - \frac{}{6}$	→	_____
2.	$\frac{7}{8} - \frac{2}{3}$	→	$\frac{}{24} - \frac{}{}$	→	_____
3.	$\frac{5}{6} - \frac{1}{4}$	→		→	_____
4.	$\frac{7}{9} - \frac{2}{3}$	→		→	_____
5.	$2\frac{7}{8} - 1\frac{1}{4}$	→	$2\frac{7}{8} - 1\frac{}{8}$	→	_____
6.	$2\frac{2}{3} - \frac{1}{2}$	→		→	_____
7.	$3\frac{1}{4} - 2\frac{1}{2}$	→		→	_____
8.	$1\frac{4}{9} - \frac{1}{3}$	→		→	_____
9.	$4\frac{2}{3} - \frac{5}{9}$	→		→	_____

C. Solve these problems in your book. Simplify your answers.

1. $\frac{11}{8} - \frac{2}{3}$

2. $\frac{9}{12} - \frac{8}{16}$

3. $\frac{1}{2} - \frac{2}{12}$

4. $\frac{7}{8} - \frac{2}{5}$

5. $5\frac{2}{3} - 2\frac{3}{5}$

6. $7\frac{5}{9} - \frac{4}{6}$

7. $\frac{3}{4} - \frac{4}{7}$

8. $\frac{7}{8} - \frac{4}{7}$

23

Dividing whole numbers by fractions

I am learning how to solve problems that involve dividing whole numbers by fractions.

A. Solve these problems. Show your working. The first one is started for you.

1. There are 4 pizzas. Each person has $\frac{2}{3}$ of a pizza. What is the maximum number of people who can share the pizzas?

$$\frac{4}{1} \div \frac{2}{3} = \frac{4}{1} \times \underline{\quad\quad} = \underline{\quad\quad} = \underline{\quad\quad}$$

4. There are 9 chocolate bars. Each person eats $\frac{3}{4}$ of one bar. What is the maximum number of people who can share the chocolate bars?

2. There are 10 bags of sweets. Each person eats $\frac{5}{8}$ of one bag. What is the maximum number of people who can share the sweets?

5. There are 6 pizzas. Each person eats $\frac{3}{4}$ of one pizza. What is the maximum number of people who can share the pizzas?

3. There are 3 pavlovas. Each person eats $\frac{3}{8}$ of one pavlova. What is the maximum number of people who can share the pavlovas?

6. There are 8 bags of sweets. Each person eats $\frac{4}{7}$ of one bag. What is the maximum number of people who can share the sweets?

B. Help the number machine to solve the problems.

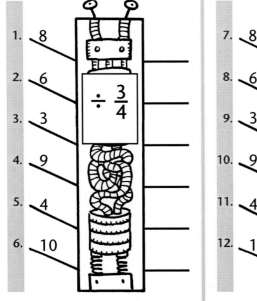

1. 8

2. 6

$\div \frac{3}{4}$

3. 3

4. 9

5. 4

6. 10

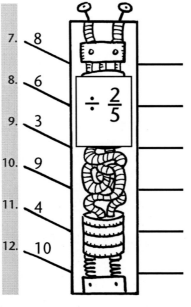

7. 8

8. 6

$\div \frac{2}{5}$

9. 3

10. 9

11. 4

12. 10

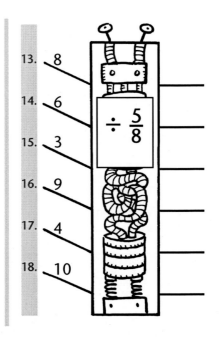

13. 8

14. 6

$\div \frac{5}{8}$

15. 3

16. 9

17. 4

18. 10

24 © Essential Resources Educational Publishers Ltd, 2009

Using estimation to check multiplication and division problems

I am learning to use estimation to check multiplication problems.

Keith has solved these problems. Check his answers using estimation. Has he absolutely – or possibly – hit the bull's eye, or has he missed the mark completely? Justify your decision. Discuss your answers with a maths buddy.

	Problem	Decision	Justification
1.	57 × 183 = 10 431	missed the mark / could be right / bull's eye	7 × 3 = 21 units column is right 60 × 200 = 12 000
2.	426 × 89 = 45 914	missed the mark / could be right / bull's eye	
3.	32.56 × 498 = 16 214.88	missed the mark / could be right / bull's eye	
4.	0.495 × 26.8 = 132.76	missed the mark / could be right / bull's eye	
5.	48.2 × 78.8 = 3 798.16	missed the mark / could be right / bull's eye	
6.	603 × 47 = 2 841	missed the mark / could be right / bull's eye	
7.	8.71 × 9.05 = 70.6255	missed the mark / could be right / bull's eye	
8.	24.29 × 258.7 = 1 639.823	missed the mark / could be right / bull's eye	
9.	472.8 × 39 = 18 556.4	missed the mark / could be right / bull's eye	
10.	33.45 × 78.7 = 2 532.515	missed the mark / could be right / bull's eye	
11.	904.8 × 31.7 = 39 682.16	missed the mark / could be right / bull's eye	

A. Estimate the answer to each of the following problems. Colour the number that is closest to your estimate.

1.	0.012 × 89.648	
	0.09	0.9
	9	90
	Reason:	

2.	64.33 ÷ 3.24463	
	20	200
	2	0.2
	Reason:	

3.	0.683 × 5.38	
	0.36	360
	36	3.6
	Reason:	

B. Estimate the answer to each of the following problems. The first one is done for you.

1. 59.28 × 63.04 ↓ ↓ 60 × 60 ≈ 360	6. 7.21 × 84.9 ↓ ↓ ___ × ___ ≈ ___	11. 23.4 × 7.6 ↓ ↓ ___ × ___ ≈ ___
2. 488.4 × 17.4 ↓ ↓ ___ × ___ ≈ ___	7. 48.69 ÷ 3.91 ↓ ↓ ___ × ___ ≈ ___	12. 36.19 × 0.942 ↓ ↓ ___ × ___ ≈ ___
3. 0.35 × 0.87 ↓ ↓ ___ × ___ ≈ ___	8. 68.7 × 51.9 ↓ ↓ ___ × ___ ≈ ___	13. 83.23 × 7.89 ↓ ↓ ___ × ___ ≈ ___
4. 39.8 × 298.2 ↓ ↓ ___ × ___ ≈ ___	9. 1.26 × 385.54 ↓ ↓ ___ × ___ ≈ ___	14. 2.058 × 379 ↓ ↓ ___ × ___ ≈ ___
5. 62.49 × 0.876 ↓ ↓ ___ × ___ ≈ ___	10. 341.231 × 7.89 ↓ ↓ ___ × ___ ≈ ___	15. 6.832 ÷ 0.576 ↓ ↓ ___ × ___ ≈ ___

C. Discuss your answers with your maths buddy.

A. Estimate the answer to each of the following problems. Colour the number that is closest to your estimate.

1.

38.526 × 12.987	
500	5 000
5	0.5
Reason:	

2.

0.8625 ÷ 0.014	
61	6 100
610	6.1
Reason:	

3.

1490 × 0.004962	
75	750
0.75	7.5
Reason:	

B. Estimate the answer to each of the following problems. The first one is done for you.

1. 47.8 × 0.63
   ↓   ↓
   _48_ × _1_ ≈ _48_

2. 7.2 × 8.9
   ↓   ↓
   ____ × ____ ≈ ____

3. 23.65 ÷ 6.9
   ↓   ↓
   ____ × ____ ≈ ____

4. 48.34 × 8.623
   ↓   ↓
   ____ × ____ ≈ ____

5. 846.7 ÷ 0.974
   ↓   ↓
   ____ × ____ ≈ ____

6. 7.982 ÷ 0.1254
   ↓   ↓
   ____ × ____ ≈ ____

7. 8.992 × 34.8
   ↓   ↓
   ____ × ____ ≈ ____

8. 68.27 ÷ 10.291
   ↓   ↓
   ____ × ____ ≈ ____

9. 0.69 ÷ 0.099
   ↓   ↓
   ____ × ____ ≈ ____

10. 84.2 × 104.001
    ↓   ↓
    ____ × ____ ≈ ____

11. 1 487 × 0.2468
    ↓   ↓
    ____ × ____ ≈ ____

12. 8 327 ÷ 9.724
    ↓   ↓
    ____ × ____ ≈ ____

13. 258.76 × 0.0012
    ↓   ↓
    ____ × ____ ≈ ____

14. 21.3 × 506.8
    ↓   ↓
    ____ × ____ ≈ ____

15. 0.36 ÷ 0.00498
    ↓   ↓
    ____ × ____ ≈ ____

C. Discuss your answers with your maths buddy.

I am learning to estimate as a way to solve decimal multiplication and division problems.

Choose the best approximate answer and state why you chose it. Discuss your answers with a maths buddy.

1. $7.532 \times 0.0014 \approx$

0.7	0.007	0.0007	0.07
Reason:			

2. $0.54 \div 9.896 \approx$

5	0.5	0.05	0.005
Reason:			

3. $0.05482 \times 68.35 \approx$

34	3.4	0.34	340
Reason:			

4. $834.9 \div 0.4989 \approx$

1 650	165	16.5	16 500
Reason:			

5. $0.6429 \div 0.0014 \approx$

60	600	6	6 000
Reason:			

6. $7\,284 \times 12.45 \approx$

730	73	7 300	73 000
Reason:			

7. $64.94 \times 0.0018 \approx$

1.3	13	0.13	0.013
Reason:			

8. $0.9846 \times 507.2 \approx$

50	5	5 000	500
Reason:			

9. $41.328 \div (80.69 \times 0.49) \approx$

100	1	1 000	10
Reason:			

10. $(620 \times 3.98) \div (0.62 \times 398) \approx$

0.1	1	10	100
Reason:			

Solving division problems by using reversals

I am learning to solve division problems using reversals.

Fill in the missing numbers. Show your working and round the calculator answers to two decimal points. The first problem is started for you.

1.	$14.79 \div \underline{\hspace{1cm}} = 4.721$	$\longmapsto$	$\underline{14.79} \div \underline{4.721} = \underline{3.13}$
2.	$\underline{\hspace{1cm}} \div 4.9811 = 2.654$	$\longmapsto$	$\underline{\hspace{1cm}} \quad \underline{\hspace{1cm}} = \underline{\hspace{1cm}}$
3.	$9.402 \div \underline{\hspace{1cm}} = 1.72$	$\longmapsto$	$\underline{\hspace{1cm}} \quad \underline{\hspace{1cm}} = \underline{\hspace{1cm}}$
4.	$33.12 \div \underline{\hspace{1cm}} = 6.421$	$\longmapsto$	$\underline{\hspace{1cm}} \quad \underline{\hspace{1cm}} = \underline{\hspace{1cm}}$
5.	$\underline{\hspace{1cm}} \div 6.981 = 1.04$	$\longmapsto$	$\underline{\hspace{1cm}} \quad \underline{\hspace{1cm}} = \underline{\hspace{1cm}}$
6.	$\underline{\hspace{1cm}} \div 3.779 = 22.61$	$\longmapsto$	$\underline{\hspace{1cm}} \quad \underline{\hspace{1cm}} = \underline{\hspace{1cm}}$
7.	$\underline{\hspace{1cm}} \div 3.941 = 14.23$	$\longmapsto$	$\underline{\hspace{1cm}} \quad \underline{\hspace{1cm}} = \underline{\hspace{1cm}}$
8.	$14.67 \div \underline{\hspace{1cm}} = 3.46$	$\longmapsto$	$\underline{\hspace{1cm}} \quad \underline{\hspace{1cm}} = \underline{\hspace{1cm}}$
9.	$70.11 \div \underline{\hspace{1cm}} = 6.21$	$\longmapsto$	$\underline{\hspace{1cm}} \quad \underline{\hspace{1cm}} = \underline{\hspace{1cm}}$
10.	$\underline{\hspace{1cm}} \div 2.0771 = 25.42$	$\longmapsto$	$\underline{\hspace{1cm}} \quad \underline{\hspace{1cm}} = \underline{\hspace{1cm}}$
11.	$98.10 \div \underline{\hspace{1cm}} = 17.3$	$\longmapsto$	$\underline{\hspace{1cm}} \quad \underline{\hspace{1cm}} = \underline{\hspace{1cm}}$
12.	$\underline{\hspace{1cm}} \div 7.9206 = 5.8$	$\longmapsto$	$\underline{\hspace{1cm}} \quad \underline{\hspace{1cm}} = \underline{\hspace{1cm}}$
13.	$8.732 \div \underline{\hspace{1cm}} = 2.6$	$\longmapsto$	$\underline{\hspace{1cm}} \quad \underline{\hspace{1cm}} = \underline{\hspace{1cm}}$
14.	$\underline{\hspace{1cm}} \div 4.4887 = 6.2$	$\longmapsto$	$\underline{\hspace{1cm}} \quad \underline{\hspace{1cm}} = \underline{\hspace{1cm}}$
15.	$59.44 \div \underline{\hspace{1cm}} = 4.9$	$\longmapsto$	$\underline{\hspace{1cm}} \quad \underline{\hspace{1cm}} = \underline{\hspace{1cm}}$
16.	$\underline{\hspace{1cm}} \div 25.2869 = 3.52$	$\longmapsto$	$\underline{\hspace{1cm}} \quad \underline{\hspace{1cm}} = \underline{\hspace{1cm}}$

Finding fractions between other fractions

I am learning to find fractions between two other fractions.

Find two fractions between the pair in the first column, using the working space to work out your answer. Circle the method you used and then write your answer in the final column. Discuss your answers with a maths buddy.

	Problem	Working space	Method	Answer
1.	$\frac{7}{9}$ and $\frac{5}{6}$		Common denominator Changed to decimals	
2.	$\frac{4}{10}$ and $\frac{2}{25}$		Common denominator Changed to decimals	
3.	$\frac{3}{4}$ and $\frac{2}{5}$		Common denominator Changed to decimals	
4.	$\frac{21}{28}$ and $\frac{20}{30}$		Common denominator Changed to decimals	
5.	$\frac{4}{5}$ and $\frac{5}{6}$		Common denominator Changed to decimals	
6.	$\frac{1}{4}$ and $\frac{4}{25}$		Common denominator Changed to decimals	
7.	$\frac{4}{6}$ and $\frac{3}{8}$		Common denominator Changed to decimals	
8.	$\frac{6}{10}$ and $\frac{3}{6}$		Common denominator Changed to decimals	
9.	$\frac{5}{40}$ and $\frac{12}{48}$		Common denominator Changed to decimals	
10.	$\frac{40}{64}$ and $\frac{15}{60}$		Common denominator Changed to decimals	
11.	$\frac{2}{7}$ and $\frac{3}{9}$		Common denominator Changed to decimals	
12.	$\frac{3}{8}$ and $\frac{2}{3}$		Common denominator Changed to decimals	
13.	$\frac{4}{5}$ and $\frac{16}{24}$		Common denominator Changed to decimals	
14.	$\frac{5}{8}$ and $\frac{3}{6}$		Common denominator Changed to decimals	

Expressing remainders from division problems in different ways

I am learning to solve division problems and express the remainder as a whole number, fraction or a decimal.

Complete this table. Simplify the fractions. The first row is done for you.

	Equation	Remainder	Fraction	Decimal
1.	$51 \div 8 =$	6 r3	$6\frac{3}{8}$	6.375
2.	$26 \div 8 =$			
3.	$61 \div 5 =$			
4.	$81 \div 6 =$			
5.	$97 \div 3 =$			
6.	$63 \div 5 =$			
7.	$70 \div 8 =$			
8.	$39 \div 9 =$			
9.	$66 \div 4 =$			
10.	$73 \div 8 =$			
11.	$82 \div 8 =$			
12.	$99 \div 4 =$			
13.	$43 \div 5 =$			
14.	$11 \div 8 =$			
15.	$163 \div 5 =$			
16.	$422 \div 6 =$			
17.	$207 \div 2 =$			
18.	$483 \div 4 =$			
19.	$781 \div 3 =$			
20.	$653 \div 2 =$			
21.	$862 \div 3 =$			
22.	$457 \div 4 =$			
23.	$205 \div 3 =$			

Finding the percentage of a whole number

I am learning to find a percentage of a whole number.

A. Complete the table. The first row has been started for you.

		10% of	1% of	25% of	50% of	5% of
1.	36	3.6				
2.	72					
3.	184					
4.	528					

B. Use the answers above to help you solve these problems.

1. 60% of 36

    50% = _____

    10% = _____

    60% = _____

5. 55% of 72

    50% = _____

    5% = _____

    55% = _____

2. 22% of 528

    20% = _____

    2% = _____

    22% = _____

6. 26% of 36

    25% = _____

    1% = _____

    26% = _____

3. 48% of 72

    50% = _____

    2% = _____

    48% = _____

7. 15% of 528

    10% = _____

    5% = _____

    15% = _____

4. 80% of 528

    50% = _____

    30% = _____

    80% = _____

    or

    100% = _____

    20% = _____

    80% = _____

8. 34% of 184

    10% = _____

    10% = _____

    10% = _____

    4% = _____

    34% = _____

Estimating percentage problems

I am learning to estimate percentage problems.

A. Choose the best approximate answer and state why you chose it. Discuss your answers with a maths buddy.

1. 24% of 1 784

50	500	35	350

Reason:

4. 61% of 698

300	420	42	30

Reason:

2. 42% of 4 160

1 240	1 680	168	124

Reason:

5. 35% of 8 062

2 800	280	3 600	36

Reason:

3. 8% of 196

28	16	7	12

Reason:

6. 79% of 304

300	240	210	280

Reason:

B. Estimate how much a customer would pay for each of the following items in the sale.

	70% off marked price	Working	Estimated cost
1.	Rug – large £289.90		
2.	Rug – hallway £129.90		
3.	Towel £18.95		
4.	Sheet set – single £36.40		
5.	Sheet set – queen £62.40		
6.	Duvet inner – single £89.60		
7.	Duvet inner – queen £145.80		

A. Choose the best approximate answer and state why you chose it. Discuss your answers with a maths buddy.

1. 17% of 285

32	48	60	28
Reason:			

4. 58% of 3 985

2 400	1 500	3 000	2 000
Reason:			

2. 29% of 3 498

1 500	720	1 280	1 050
Reason:			

5. 7% of 244

9	18	14	24
Reason:			

3. 39% of 8 920

2 500	3 500	3 000	4 000
Reason:			

6. 45% of 6 379

2 820	3 560	2 500	3 620
Reason:			

B. Estimate how much a customer would pay for each of the following items in the sale.

	60% off marked price	Working	Estimated cost
1.	Electric frying pan £139.40		
2.	CD player £224.30		
3.	Electric jug £89.90		
4.	Waffle maker £74.50		
5.	Electric clock £28.98		
6.	16" TV £479.90		
7.	Toaster £64.56		

I am learning to estimate percentages of whole numbers and decimals.

Estimate the answers to the following problems. Discuss your answers with a maths buddy.

	Problem	Working	Estimation
1.	48% of 63	48 is close to 50 63 ≈ 60 50% of 60 is 30	30
2.	62% of 130		
3.	27% of 72		
4.	84% of 32		
5.	17% of 36.4		
6.	49% of 27.48		
7.	35% of 45.8		
8.	79% of £92.00		
9.	32% of £87.00		
10.	54 % of £88.00		
11.	93% of £43.00		

Estimate the answers to the following problems. Discuss your answers with a maths buddy.

	Problem	Working	Estimation
1.	16.5% of £84.60	10% ≈ 8.40 5% ≈ 4.20 est = 8.40 + 4.20	£12.60
2.	26.7% of £369.40		
3.	57% of £984.00		
4.	48% of £562.35		
5.	19% of £26.49		
6.	72.3% of £1692.00		
7.	45.3% of £69.38		
8.	40.6% of £382.00		
9.	82.7% of £362.00		
10.	1.5% of £23.76		

I am learning to estimate percentages of whole numbers and decimals.

A. Estimate the answers to the following problems. Colour the number that is closest to your estimate.

1.

7.9% of £92.00	
90p	£9.00
£9.20	92p

Reason:

2.

57.9% of £88.90	
£60.00	£5.40
£54.00	£6.00

Reason:

3.

92.6% of £148.00	
£10.00	£13.50
£100.00	£135.00

Reason:

B. Estimate the answers to the following problems. Discuss your answers with a maths buddy.

	Problem	Working	Estimation
1.	27% of £376.54		
2.	69.5% of £37.45		
3.	5.6% of £126.00		
4.	68.5% of £79.30		
5.	29.5% of £615.45		
6.	37.2% of £89.90		
7.	21.7% of £46.50		
8.	51.9% of £324.15		

A. Estimate the answers to the following problems.

	Problem	Working	Estimation
1.	42 out of 63	Is close to 40 out of 60, which is $\frac{2}{3}$ which is 0.66	66%
2.	27 out of 39		
3.	72 out of 84		
4.	28 out of 64		
5.	9 out of 41		
6.	35 out of 52		

B. Complete the table.

	Problem	Working	Estimation of %
1.	Erin got 36 out of 52 correct in her maths test. Estimate the percentage she got right.		%
2.	Stefan shot 18 out of 24 attempts at goal. Estimate the percentage he missed.		%
3.	Lewis worked 24 out of the possible 30 hours. Estimate the percentage of hours Lewis **didn't** work.		%
4.	Rebecca ate 41 out of 56 jelly beans. Estimate the percentage of jelly beans she ate.		%
5.	Dylan collected 48 out of 66 cards. Estimate the percentage of cards he collected.		%
6.	Michelle made 14 out of 18 pies. Estimate the percentage of pies she **didn't** make.		%

C. Discuss your answers with your maths buddy.

38

Solving percentage problems involving inflation

I am learning to solve percentage problems involving inflation.

A. If inflation is 10% each year, complete the table to show the amount each value increases by over time.

		After 1 year	After 2 years	After 3 years	After 5 years
1.	£1.00				
2.	£5.00				
3.	£4.00				
4.	£5.50				

B. If inflation is 25% each year, complete the table to show the amount each value increases by over time.

		After 1 year	After 2 years	After 3 years	After 5 years
1.	£1.00				
2.	£5.00				
3.	£4.00				
4.	£6.50				

C. If inflation is 12% each year, complete the table to show the amount each value increases by over time.

		After 1 year	After 2 years	After 3 years	After 5 years
1.	£1.00				
2.	£5.00				
3.	£4.00				
4.	£8.50				

I am learning to solve percentage problems involving inflation.

1. Rob purchases a new car for £30 000.00. If annual inflation runs at 10%, how much will the equivalent car cost in:

1 year	5 years	10 years

2. Rob purchases a house for £320 000.00. If annual inflation runs at 5%, how much will the equivalent house cost in:

1 year	5 years	10 years

3. Rob purchases a boat for £18 000.00. If annual inflation runs at 15%, how much will the equivalent boat cost in:

1 year	5 years	10 years

4. Rob purchases a diamond ring for £12 000.00. If annual inflation runs at 5%, how much will the equivalent ring cost in:

1 year	5 years	10 years

1.	Chris purchases a new racing bike for £5 000.00. If annual inflation runs at 10%, how much will the equivalent bike cost in:		
	1 year	**5 years**	**10 years**

2.	Diggs purchases a new set of golf clubs for £6 000.00. If annual inflation runs at 5%, how much will the equivalent set cost in:		
	1 year	**5 years**	**10 years**

3.	Marty purchases a kayak for £3 000.00. If annual inflation runs at 15%, how much will the equivalent kayak cost in:		
	1 year	**5 years**	**10 years**

4.	Julie purchases a skateboard for £300.00. If annual inflation runs at 5%, how much will the equivalent skateboard cost in:		
	1 year	**5 years**	**10 years**

Solving percentage problems

I am learning to solve percentage problems.

Fi and Max own a sports shop specialising in ski and snowboard gear. Work out how much they sell each item for. Round the answer to two decimal places. The first row is started for you.

	Cost price	Mark up %	Mark up in £	Selling price
1.	Ski boots £258.67	15.6%	0.156 × 258.67 = _____	258.67 + _____ = _____
2.	Skis £420.15	7.8%		
3.	Goggles £15.50	26.8%		
4.	Snowboard £364.25	17.8%		
5.	Jacket £192.87	25%		
6.	Gloves £26.40	16%		
7.	Snowboarding boots £185.60	24.5%		
8.	Wrist guards £35.70	38.4%		
9.	Helmet £67.00	5.6%		
10.	Ski binding £120.00	17.5%		
11.	Snowboard binding £136.80	24.3%		
12.	Ski boots £157.80	36.7%		
13.	Ski poles £72.85	4%		
14.	Hat £15.50	12.5%		

© Essential Resources Educational Publishers Ltd, 2009

A. George and Marta's surf shop is having a pre-Christmas sale. Work out how much they sell each item for. Round the answer to two decimal places. The first one is started for you.

	Cost price	Discount %	Discount in £	Selling price
1.	Long board £859.99	18%	0.18 × 859.99 = _____	859.99 – _____ = _____
2.	Short board £764.49	11%		
3.	Wet suit £268.75	15%		
4.	Booties £45.65	8%		
5.	Gloves £78.50	25%		
6.	Wax £8.40	14%		
7.	Long board cover £85.63	28%		
8.	Short board cover £72.94	28%		
9.	Leg rope £26.50	12%		
10.	Vest £174.25	24%		
11.	Rashie £49.65	15%		
12.	Surf magazine £5.95	12%		

Activity cards

The instructions to play the games in this section have been presented on a separate page for the pupils so that they can be photocopied on to card and placed with the relevant game. They can then be given to the children to encourage independence.

Beans game (page 47)

The aim of this game is to reinforce knowledge of fraction, decimal and percentage conversions.

To **make:**

- copy cards onto coloured paper

- laminate and cut out cards

- store in a ziplock bag along with four bean bags and a copy of the rules.

Note: a blank template can be drawn up for the teacher or children to make a variety of families of facts for an extra game.

Warning: this game is very exciting and can create some noise.

Bigger/smaller (page 52)

The aim of this game is to reinforce counting forwards and backwards word sequences of decimal numbers.

To **make:**

- make a dice with the following numbers on it:

    100, 10, 1, 0.1, 0.01, 0.001

    or

    $100, 10, 1, \frac{1}{10}, \frac{1}{100}, \frac{1}{1000}$

- photocopy, laminate and cut the number cards

- store in a ziplock bag along with a copy of the rules.

Fraction game (page 50)

The aim of this game is to reinforce adding and subtracting fractions.

To **make:**

- enlarge game board onto A3 paper and laminate

- make a dice with + and − on alternate sides

- store in a ziplock bag along with counters and a copy of the rules.

Note: a blank template has been included for the teacher or children to make an alternative game board.

Pupil instructions

Beans game

Equipment required:

- four bean bags
- game cards

To **play** with five players:

- place four bean bags in the centre
- shuffle and deal out all the cards
- the aim is to collect an equivalent set containing a fraction card, a decimal card and a percentage card

$$\text{eg, } 0.5, 50\%, \frac{1}{2}$$

- each person passes an unwanted card to the person on the left, picks up and checks the card passed to them, and then passes any unwanted card to the next person (all done very quickly)
- when an equivalent set is collected, the collector takes a bean bag
- the other four players try to take one of the remaining three bean bags
- the collector then shows the equivalent set to the other players to verify the family.

Each time a player is the first to get a bean bag, they get one letter towards the spelling of the word *beans*. The first player to spell the word *beans* is the winner.

I am learning to add and subtract fractions.

Fraction game

Equipment required:

- dice
- + − dice
- game board
- a counter for each player

To **play** with two players:

- roll a dice – it will show the number that you have to make
- put your counter on any one of the fractions on the game board
- each player takes a turn to move their counter
- roll the + − dice and then choose a fraction along the provided path to either add to or subtract from the fraction that you have just been on.

The first player to reach their number is the winner.

Bigger/smaller

Equipment required:

- _____ dice

- game cards

To **play**:

- place the number cards face down

- the first player rolls the dice and then picks up a number card

- based on the amount on the dice, the player says the number that comes that amount before and the number that comes that amount after the number on the card

- each correct answer gains one point. The person with the most points at the end is the winner.

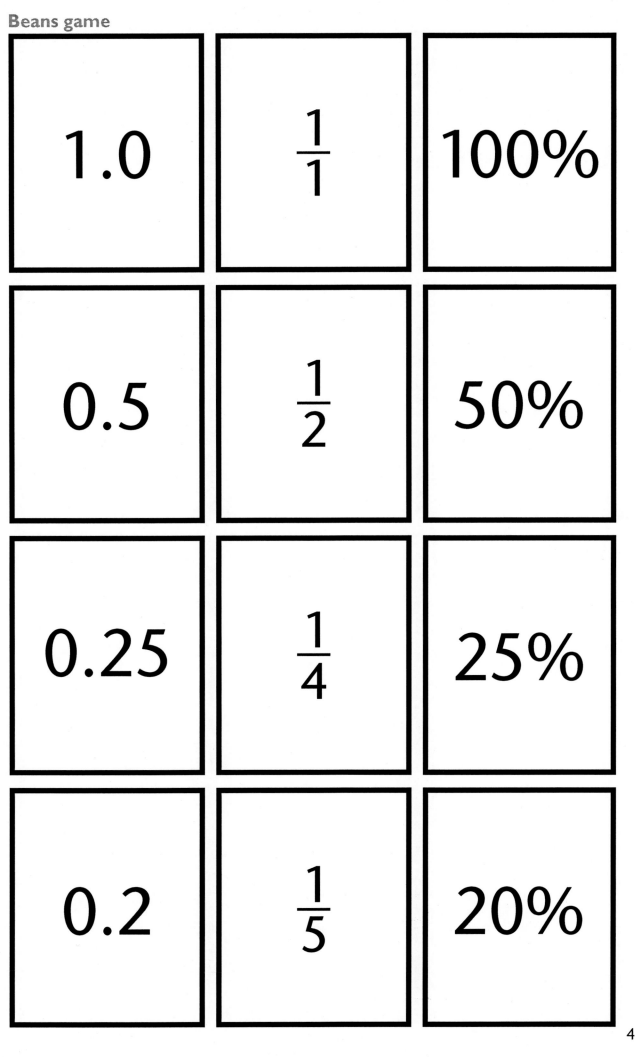

1.0	$\dfrac{1}{1}$	100%
0.5	$\dfrac{1}{2}$	50%
0.25	$\dfrac{1}{4}$	25%
0.2	$\dfrac{1}{5}$	20%

0.333	$\frac{1}{3}$	33.3%
0.125	$\frac{1}{8}$	12.5%
0.1	$\frac{1}{10}$	10%
0.66	$\frac{2}{3}$	66.6%

0.75	$\frac{3}{4}$	75%
0.4	$\frac{2}{5}$	40%
0.6	$\frac{3}{5}$	60%
0.375	$\frac{3}{8}$	37.5%

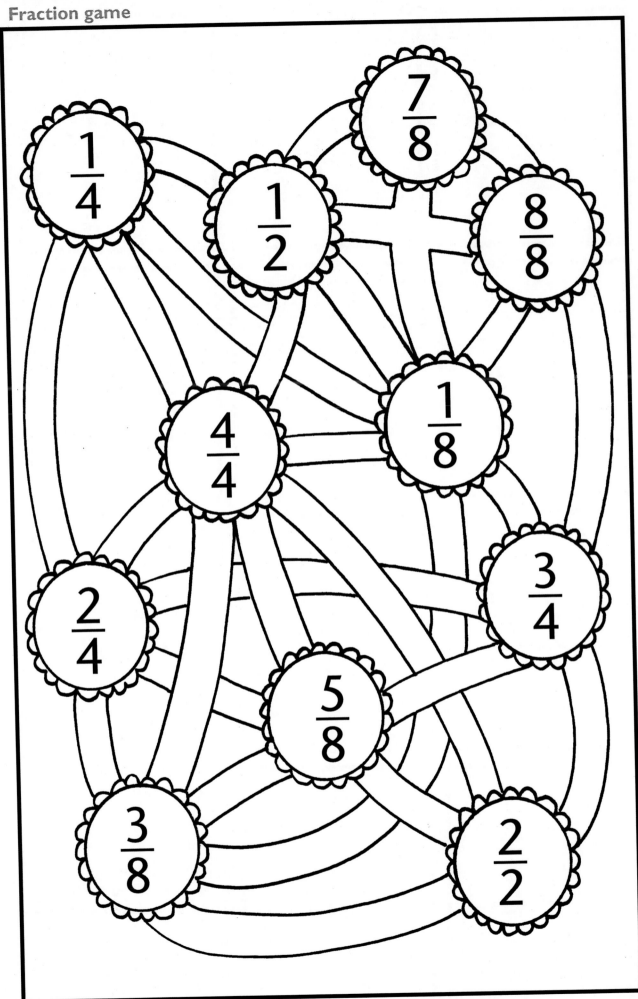

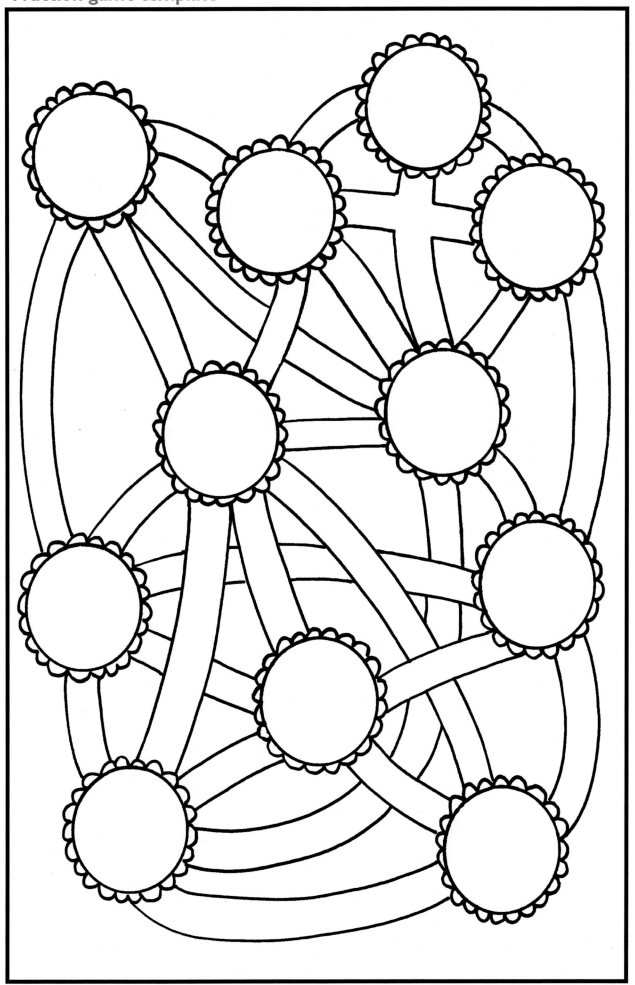

5.81632	3.65794
9.65812	7.02564
65.6324	71.0009
953.004	0.35789
3.68946	6.31682
7.36125	9.82546
4.52631	8.55499

7.35649	4.20159
99.3939	0.21032
2.03690	1.09024
3.06879	9.99999
5.39649	2.12358
3.72910	4.08971
7.36904	0.00697

Answers

Page 5

A1. 6.324891, 6.324981, 6.32981, 6.32986

2.

3. 6.32, 6.33, 6.33, 6.32

B1. 2.787922, 2.787977, 2.788001, 2.788010

2.

3. 2.79, 2.79, 2.79, 2.79

C1. 0.27523, 0.27559, 0.27564, 0.27584

2.

3. 0.28, 0.28, 0.28, 0.28

Page 6

A1. 2.324891, 2.324981, 2.32981, 2.32986

2.

3. 2.32, 2.33, 2.33, 2.32

B1. 77.2292, 77.2308, 77.2336, 77.2351

2.

3. 77.23, 77.23, 77.24, 77.23

C1. 0.022154, 0.022169, 0.022177, 0.022185

2.

3. 0.02, 0.02, 0.02, 0.02

Page 7

1. 0.62, $\frac{5}{8}$, 75%

2. 0.54, 60%, $\frac{2}{3}$

3. 10%, $\frac{4}{32}$, 0.25

4. $\frac{4}{5}$, $\frac{84}{100}$, 0.85

5. $\frac{3}{5}$, 65%, 0.7

6. 0.2, $\frac{2}{8}$, 26%

7. 15%, 0.2, $\frac{16}{64}$

8. $\frac{24}{40}$, 65%, 0.75

9. 65%, $\frac{28}{42}$, 0.7

10. 0.1, $\frac{5}{40}$, 15%

11. 59%, 0.6, $\frac{4}{6}$

12. 0.3, 33%, $\frac{3}{8}$

Page 8

1. 0.036, 4%, 0.1, $\frac{1}{8}$, 15%, $\frac{4}{6}$, $\frac{5}{4}$, 1.473, 150%

2. 20%, 0.25, $\frac{3}{8}$, 0.398, 60%, 0.602, $\frac{6}{8}$, $\frac{8}{10}$, 84%

3. 21%, $\frac{5}{20}$, 0.459, 0.46, 50%, $\frac{10}{16}$, 120%, 1.72, $\frac{7}{4}$

4. 0.04, 9%, 40%, $\frac{9}{15}$, 0.65, $\frac{2}{3}$, 70%, $\frac{60}{80}$, 0.9

Page 8 continued

5. 0.125, $\frac{3}{15}$, 25%, 0.33, $\frac{12}{32}$, 65%, 100%, 1.25, $\frac{11}{8}$

6. 0.008, 7%, $\frac{1}{8}$, 0.2, 24%, $\frac{15}{60}$, $\frac{15}{40}$, 0.79, 80%

7. $\frac{5}{40}$, 15%, 25%, 0.35, $\frac{14}{10}$, 1.45, $\frac{6}{4}$, 1.6 and 160%

Page 9

A1.	>, <	8.	>, >	15.	<, >	22.	>, >
2.	<, >	9.	>, <	16.	=, >	23.	<, >
3.	>, >	10.	<, <	17.	>, >	24.	<, <
4.	<, <	11.	=, >	18.	>, <	25.	=, =
5.	>, >	12.	>, <	19.	>, <	26.	>, >
6.	=, <	13.	<, =	20.	<, >	27.	=, >
7.	=, <	14.	<, >	21.	>, =	28.	=, >

B1. 0.1, 15%, 0.2 and $\frac{4}{20}$, 33%, $\frac{9}{24}$, 50%, 0.62, $\frac{12}{18}$

2. $\frac{8}{12}$, 0.7, 75%, 0.8, 90%, $\frac{9}{8}$, 120%, $\frac{4}{3}$, 1.4

Page 10

1. 0.099, 0.109, 0.119, 0.139, 0.149, 0.159
2. 2.039, 2.049, 2.059, 2.079, 2.089, 2.099
3. 8.006, 8.016, 8.026, 8.046, 8.056, 8.066
4. 0.039, 0.049, 0.059, 0.079, 0.089, 0.099
5. 0.098, 0.108, 0.118, 0.138, 0.148, 0.158
6. 0.941, 0.951, 0.961, 0.981, 0.991, 1.001
7. 0.969, 0.979, 0.989, 1.009, 1.019, 1.029
8. 0.449, 0.459, 0.469, 0.489, 0.499, 0.509
9. 3.991, 4.001, 4.011, 4.031, 4.041, 4.051
10. 7.973, 7.983, 7.993, 8.013, 8.023, 8.033
11. 7.018, 7.028, 7.038, 7.058, 7.068, 7.078
12. 0.119, 0.129, 0.139, 0.159, 0.169, 0.179
13. 5.998, 6.008, 6.018, 6.038, 6.048, 6.058
14. 0.129, 0.139, 0.149, 0.169, 0.179, 0.189
15. 4.005, 4.015, 4.025, 4.045, 4.055, 4.065
16. 2.366, 2.376, 2.386, 2.406, 2.416, 2.426
17. 0.979, 0.989, 0.999, 1.019, 1.029, 1.039
18. 8.195, 8.205, 8.215, 8.235, 8.245, 8.255
19. 0.518, 0.528, 0.538, 0.558, 0.568, 0.578
20. 6.009, 6.019, 6.029, 6.049, 6.059, 6.069
21. 4.575, 4.585, 4.595, 4.615, 4.625, 4.635
22. 0.994, 1.004, 1.014, 1.034, 1.044, 1.054
23. 3.951, 3.961, 3.971, 3.991, 4.001, 4.011
24. 0.971, 0.981, 0.991, 1.011, 1.021, 1.031

Page 11

#	A	#	B
A1.	40	B1.	10^1
2.	11	2.	10^1
3.	1 100	3.	10^2
4.	9 500	4.	10^2
5.	7 300	5.	10^2
6.	520	6.	10^1
7.	300	7.	10^3
8.	5.1	8.	10^1
9.	870	9.	10^1
10.	49	10.	10^1
11.	47	11.	10^2
12.	20	12.	10^2
13.	290	13.	10^1
14.	5 400	14.	10^2
15.	910	15.	10^2
16.	7 700	16.	10^1

C1. 730 hours
2. 6 500 hours

Page 12

#	A	#	B
A1.	34	B1.	10^0
2.	14 000	2.	10^3
3.	6 900	3.	10^1
4.	91 000	4.	10^2
5.	820 000	5.	10^2
6.	5 300	6.	10^1
7.	1	7.	10^1
8.	5 100 000	8.	10^2
9.	14 000	9.	10^2
10.	5 000	10.	10^1
11.	100 000	11.	10^2
12.	6 400 000	12.	10^1
13.	73 000	13.	10^0
14.	560 000	14.	10^3
15.	15 000	15.	10^1
16.	80	16.	10^5

C1. 3 000 km
2. 50 000 km

Page 13

#	A	#	B
A1.	256	B1.	2 187
2.	15 625	2.	100 000
3.	64	3.	243
4.	1 000 000	4.	3 125
5.	512	5.	6 561
6.	1 000 000 000	6.	125

Page 14

#	A	#		#	
A1.	64	5.	9	3.	25
2.	8	6.	5	4.	64
3.	9	B1.	64	5.	3
4.	2	2.	256	6.	65 536

Page 15

#	A	#	B
A1.	75%	B1.	37.5%
2.	66.67%	2.	66.67%
3.	25%	3.	80%
4.	60%	4.	75%
5.	37.5%	5.	80%
6.	80%	6.	62.5%
7.	125%	7.	60%
8.	62.5%	8.	33.33%
9.	40%		
10.	75%		
11.	50%		
12.	87.5%		
13.	60%		
14.	125%		

Page 16

1. Disagree. 2, 3, 4, 6, 9
2. Disagree. 5
3. Agree.
4. Disagree. 2, 3, 4, 6
5. Agree.
6. Disagree. 2, 3, 4, 6, 9
7. Disagree. 2, 3, 5, 6, 9, 10, 15
8. Disagree. 2, 4

Page 18

A1. 16:8, 4:2, 2:1
2. 7:2, 28:8, 70:20
3. 4:20, 12:60, 1:5
4. 2:1, 12:6, 24:12
5. 3:2, 18:12, 6:4
6. 20:12, 10:6, 35:21

#	B	#		#	
B1.	i	5.	h	9.	b
2.	c	6.	j	10.	a
3.	e	7.	g	11.	d
4.	k	8.	f		

#	C	#		#	
C1.	36, 9	4.	8, 2	7.	20, 5
2.	44, 11	5.	28, 7	8.	16, 4
3.	56, 14	6.	24, 6		

Page 19

A1. 2 000, 1 000, 250
2. 50, 1000, 500, 125
3. 25, 2 500, 500, 62.5

Page 19 continued

4. 5, 500, 50, 12.5
5. 1, 100, 20, 10

#	B	#	
B1.	300:200	2.	£90

#	C	#	
C1.	2, 4, 8, 2	4.	9, 6, 12, 3
2.	12, 4, 16, 4	5.	27, 9, 18, 36
3.	15, 5, 10, 5	6.	7, 14, 28, 7

Page 20

#	A	#	B	#	C
A1.	8	B1.	$\frac{19}{18}$	C1.	$2\frac{21}{40}$
2.	10	2.	$\frac{13}{12}$	2.	$\frac{31}{40}$
3.	36	3.	$\frac{9}{9}$		
4.	20	4.	$\frac{17}{24}$		
5.	15	5.	$\frac{13}{10}$		
6.	9	6.	$\frac{11}{15}$		

Page 21

#	A	#	B	#	C
A1.	12	B1.	$\frac{44}{40}$	C1.	$2\frac{5}{24}$
2.	40	2.	$\frac{37}{30}$	2.	$2\frac{1}{12}$
3.	60	3.	$\frac{17}{12}$		
4.	18	4.	$\frac{23}{24}$		
5.	24	5.	$\frac{27}{20}$		
6.	30	6.	$\frac{61}{36}$		

Page 22

A1. $\frac{4}{5} + \frac{5}{6} = \frac{24}{30} + \frac{25}{30} = \frac{49}{30} = 1\frac{19}{30}$

2. $\frac{2}{3} - \frac{1}{4} = \frac{8}{12} - \frac{3}{12} = \frac{5}{12}$

3. $\frac{2}{5} + \frac{1}{3} = \frac{6}{15} + \frac{5}{15} = \frac{11}{15}$

4. $\frac{7}{9} - \frac{1}{2} = \frac{14}{18} - \frac{9}{18} = \frac{5}{18}$

5. $\frac{3}{8} + \frac{2}{3} = \frac{9}{24} + \frac{16}{24} = \frac{25}{40} = 1\frac{1}{24}$

6. $\frac{6}{8} - \frac{2}{5} = \frac{30}{40} - \frac{16}{40} = \frac{14}{40}$

7. $\frac{3}{4} - \frac{2}{6} = \frac{9}{12} - \frac{4}{12} = \frac{5}{12}$

8. $\frac{2}{3} + \frac{3}{5} = \frac{10}{15} + \frac{9}{15} = \frac{19}{15} = 1\frac{4}{15}$

B1. $\frac{3}{7} + \frac{1}{3} = \frac{16}{21}$

2. $\frac{7}{9} - \frac{2}{3} = \frac{1}{9}$

3. $\frac{2}{3} - \frac{1}{5} = \frac{7}{15}$

4. $\frac{2}{5} + \frac{3}{8} = \frac{31}{40}$

5. $\frac{7}{9} - \frac{3}{4} = \frac{1}{36}$

6. $\frac{6}{9} - \frac{1}{2} = \frac{3}{18}$

7. $\frac{2}{5} + \frac{2}{6} = \frac{22}{30}$

8. $\frac{3}{5} + \frac{1}{2} = \frac{11}{10}$

Page 23

A1. $36, \frac{9}{36}, \frac{24}{36}, \frac{16}{36}$

2. $30, \frac{15}{30}, \frac{18}{30}, \frac{20}{30}$

3. $24, \frac{9}{24}, \frac{12}{24}, \frac{16}{24}$

4. $40, \frac{8}{40}, \frac{30}{40}, \frac{20}{40}$

B1.	$\frac{1}{6}$	C1.	$\frac{17}{24}$
2.	$\frac{5}{24}$	2.	$\frac{1}{4}$
3.	$\frac{7}{12}$	3.	$\frac{1}{3}$
4.	$\frac{1}{9}$	4.	$\frac{19}{40}$
5.	$1\frac{5}{8}$	5.	$3\frac{1}{15}$
6.	$2\frac{1}{6}$	6.	$6\frac{8}{9}$
7.	$\frac{3}{4}$	7.	$\frac{5}{28}$
8.	$1\frac{1}{9}$	8.	$\frac{17}{56}$
9.	$4\frac{1}{9}$		

Page 24

A1.	6	B7.	20
2.	16	8.	15
3.	8	9.	$7\frac{1}{2}$
4.	12	10.	$22\frac{1}{2}$
5.	8	11.	10
6.	14	12.	25
B1.	$10\frac{2}{3}$	13.	$12\frac{4}{5}$
2.	8	14.	$9\frac{3}{5}$
3.	4	15.	$4\frac{4}{5}$
4.	12	16.	$14\frac{2}{5}$
5.	$5\frac{1}{3}$	17.	$6\frac{2}{5}$
6.	$13\frac{1}{3}$	18.	16

Page 29

1.	3.13	9.	11.29
2.	13.22	10.	52.80
3.	5.47	11.	5.67
4.	5.16	12.	45.94
5.	7.26	13.	3.36
6.	85.44	14.	27.83
7.	56.08	15.	12.13
8.	4.24	16.	89.01

Page 31

A2.	3 r2	$3\frac{1}{4}$	3.25
3.	12 r1	$12\frac{1}{5}$	12.2
4.	13 r3	$13\frac{1}{2}$	13.5
5.	32 r1	$32\frac{1}{3}$	32.333
6.	12 r3	$12\frac{3}{5}$	12.6
7.	8 r6	$8\frac{3}{4}$	8.75
8.	4 r3	$4\frac{1}{3}$	4.333
9.	16 r2	$16\frac{1}{2}$	16.5
10.	9 r1	$9\frac{1}{8}$	9.125
11.	10 r2	$10\frac{1}{4}$	10.25
12.	24 r3	$24\frac{3}{4}$	24.75
13.	8 r3	$8\frac{3}{5}$	8.6
14.	1 r3	$1\frac{3}{8}$	1.375
15.	32 r3	$32\frac{3}{5}$	32.6
16.	70 r2	$70\frac{1}{3}$	70.333
17.	103 r1	$103\frac{1}{2}$	103.5
18.	120 r3	$120\frac{3}{4}$	120.75
19.	260 r1	$260\frac{1}{3}$	260.333
20.	326 r1	$326\frac{1}{2}$	326.5
21.	287 r1	$287\frac{1}{3}$	287.333
22.	114 r1	$114\frac{1}{4}$	114.25
23.	68 r1	$68\frac{1}{3}$	68.333

Page 32

A1. 3.6, 0.36, 9, 18, 1.8
2. 7.2, 0.72, 18, 36, 3.6
3. 18.4, 1.84, 46, 92, 9.2
4. 52.8, 5.28, 132, 264, 26.4

B1.	21.6	5.	39.60
2.	116.16	6.	9.36
3.	34.56	7.	79.2
4.	422.40	8.	62.56

Page 39

A1. £1.10, £1.21, £1.32, £1.60
2. £5.50, £6.05, £6.66, £8.06
3. £4.40, £4.84, £5.32, £6.44
4. £6.05, £6.66, £7.33, £8.87
B1. £1.25, £1.56, £1.95, £3.05
2. £6.25, £7.81, £9.76, £15.25
3. £5.00, £6.25, £7.81, £12.20
4. £8.13, £10.16, £12.70, £19.85
C1. £1.12, £1.25, £1.40, £1.76
2. £5.60, £6.27, £7.02, £8.80

Page 39 continued

C3. £4.48, £5.02, £5.62, £7.04
4. £9.52, £10.66, £11.94, £14.97

Page 40

1. £33 000.00, £48 315.30, £77 812.27
2. £336 000.00, £408 410.10, £521 246.28
3. £20 700.00, £36 204.43, £72 820.04
4. £12 600.00, £15 315.38, £19 546.74

Page 41

1. £5 500.00, £8 052.55, £12 968.71
2. £6 300.00, £7 657.69, £9 773.37
3. £3 450.00, £6 034.07, £12 136.67
4. £315.00, £382.88, £488.67

Page 42

1.	£40.35 £299.02
2.	£32.77, £452.92
3.	£4.15, £19.65
4.	£64.84, £429.09
5.	£48.22, £241.09
6.	£4.22, £30.62
7.	£45.47, £231.07
8.	£13.71, £49.41
9.	£3.75, £70.75
10.	£21.00, £141.00
11.	£33.24, £170.04
12.	£57.91, £215.71
13.	£2.91, £75.76
14.	£1.94, £17.44

Page 43

1.	£154.80, £705.19
2.	£84.09, £680.40
3.	£40.31, £228.44
4.	£3.65, £42.00
5.	£19.62, £58.88
6.	£1.18, £7.22
7.	£23.98, £61.65
8.	£20.42, £52.52
9.	£3.18, £23.32
10.	£41.82, £132.43
11.	£7.45, £42.20
12.	£0.71, £5.24